My Name Makes Me Feel Special

Written & Illustrated by

Sharifa Louis

Printed in the United States of America

First Printing, 2020

ISBN 978-0-578-66903-8

This book is dedicated

To my Husband my biggest supporter and motivator.

To my children and my granddaughter, my floor is your ceiling.

To every child with a unique name, whether you know the

meaning or not, you are created for destiny and purpose.

To my Mother and Father who had the vision to give me a

name so that I could walk out my purpose on the earth.

"Goodbye, Baby, have a wonderful first day of 3rd grade. You're going to have a terrific school year." Sharifa's mom said.

"Thanks Mom, I will."

Sharifa was so excited to start the 3rd grade. She couldn't wait to meet her new classmates and her new teacher, Mrs. Labowski.

"Good Morning Class!" Mrs. Labowski said. "Welcome to the 3rd grade. I'm going to take attendance. When I call your name say "present." Mrs. Labowski began calling the children's names alphabetically by everyone's first name.

Mrs. Labowski called Corin, and then Jonathan. Sharifa started to think about how her past teachers said her name wrong in front of the whole class.

Mrs. Labowski continued, "Sally Jo."

Sharifa knew her name was coming up soon. Mrs. Labowski tried to pronounce Sharifa's name. "Sha-rif-a, Shafa, Sha-fia, Sharifer?" "It's Sha-ri-fa."

8

Sharifa said, "Present."

Wild laughter filled the room!
Sharifa heard the other children
repeating her name the wrong
way.

"Shafa?" Corin said laughing.

Jonathan yelled, "Shafia?!"

Sally Jo whispered loud enough for others to hear her, "Sharifer? It sounds like a plant!"

The rest of the class laughed even louder. Mrs. Labowski told the class to settle down and she finished the attendance.

Sharifa bit her lip. She felt ashamed, embarrassed, and upset.

Sharifa wished her parents wouldn't have named her the dumb name anyway.

When Sharifa arrived home after school, she was so upset that she ran straight to her bedroom. Sharifa's mom heard her and came into her room.

"What's wrong sweetheart?"

"I hate my name!"

"The Teacher said my name wrong and all the kids in the class laughed and made fun of me. Why did you name me Sharifa anyway? Someone said it sounds like a plant. I hate it! When I grow up, I'm going to change my name."

Sharifa's mom hugged her and said, "Sharifa is a beautiful name. Just like you. Your father and I named you Sharifa because of the meaning."

Sharifa (Sha-ree-fa) means DISTINGUISHED, Zakiya (Zah-kee-yuh) means INTELLIGENT, Siti (Cee-tee) means LADY."

"My beautiful daughter, you are a
Distinguished, Intelligent, Lady
and I hope one day you'll love
your name.
Please don't ever change it.

Sharifa felt much better after
talking to her mom.

The next day at school, Mrs. Labowski gave the class an assignment. "Class, your first homework assignment is to write two paragraphs about what makes you special." Sharifa knew what she would write about. She went home and wrote about her name, Sharifa Zakiya Siti.

The next day, Sharifa felt confident about sharing her assignment. She couldn't wait for Mrs. Labowski to call on her. When she did, Sharifa stood up at her desk and read her paper.

Sharifa   Mrs. Labowski

What makes me special is my name. Sharifa Zakiya Siti. My name is Swahili and it means Distinguished Intelligent Lady.

My parents named me because of the meaning. Sharifa means distinguished. Zakiya means intelligent and Siti means lady. My name may be different, but I'm proud that my name means something special. Because I am special.

Jonathan, Corin, and Sally Jo gathered around Sharifa in excitement! Jonathan said "Wow, your name is cool!"

"Yea," said Sally Jo. Corin gave Sharifa a high five and said, "Thanks for sharing about your name. I'm going to ask my parents what my name means when I go home."

Sharifa knew her name was different, but it made her feel special knowing that her parents gave her a name that meant something so great. It made her feel proud.

<u>Note to parents, guardians, and teachers</u>:

Reading this book with children is the first step in helping them to be confident about their unique names. You can use these questions as a guide to facilitating open dialogue with children.

1. Can I tell you the story of how your name was chosen for you?

2. When Sharifa got teased for her name in the book, how did it make her feel?

3. Have you ever felt like Sharifa about your name?

4. Tell me about a time when you were teased about your name? How did it make you feel?

5. What are some ways we can deal with this if it happens again?

Definition of *distinguished*

1: marked by eminence, distinction, or excellence
distinguished leadership, our *distinguished* guest

2: befitting an eminent persona *distinguished* setting

Definition of *intelligent*

1 a: having or indicating a high or satisfactory degree of
intelligence and mental capacity

   b: revealing or reflecting good judgment or sound
thought:
 skillful

2 a: possessing intelligence

Definition of *lady*

1 a: a woman having proprietary rights or authority
especially as a feudal superior

   b: a woman receiving the homage or devotion of a
knight

2 a: a woman of superior social position

   b: a woman of refinement and gentle manners

When I created the organization Distinguished Intelligent Lady the first thing I thought was I want ladies of all ages, especially young girls, to know that there is power in their words. The old saying, "Sticks and Stones may break my bones, but words will never hurt me," is so untrue. Words can be very hurtful and harmful to children when used the wrong way. Proverbs 18:21 says, "Death and life are in the power of the tongue" (Holy Bible, KJV).

If your child has a unique name and you can't find the meaning in a book or online, pray about what your child's name means, so they have something to connect to that is positive.

In the process of writing this book, I thought, why not teach children to speak life over themselves by giving them positive daily affirmations. Affirmations help to build confidence, assurance, self-determination, and courage.

If your child is discouraged, read the affirmations aloud with them daily and watch their confidence come alive.

Positive Affirmations for your child

I am brave.

I am courageous.

I am strong.

I am loved.

I matter, no matter what.

I am awesome.

I belong.

I will stand tall.

I bring joy to the world.

I can get through difficult things.

My name is unique, special, and extraordinary.

I am proud to have my name.

Note to parents and teachers: Help children discover the special meaning of their name. Feel free to make copies or go to fb.me/Mynamemakesmefeelspecialbook to download and print extra copies for classroom use.

MY NAME IS:

My Name Means:

It makes me feel special

Made in the USA
San Bernardino, CA
07 July 2020